Dealing With

BULLYING

by Jane Lacey

Illustrated by Venitia Dean

W

FRANKLIN WATTS

LONDON • SYDNEY

Franklin Watts
First published in Great Britain in 2017 by The Watts Publishing Group

Credits
Series Editor: Sarah Peutrill
Series Design: Collaborate

ISBN 978 1 4451 5748 1

Printed in China

Franklin Watts
An imprint of
Hachette Children's Group
Part of The Watts Publishing Group
Carmelite House
50 Victoria Embankment
London EC4Y 0DZ

An Hachette UK Company
www.hachette.co.uk

www.franklinwatts.co.uk

MIX
Paper from
responsible sources
FSC® C104740

Contents

I FEEL LEFT OUT

Olivia's friends don't ask her to join in with them any more. They say unkind things to her. When this happens, she feels lonely and left out.

Olivia

Olivia's story

I used to play with my friends every playtime. We had really good fun. But now, when I ask if I can play too, they say, "You can't play with us!"

In class, my friends giggle together but they won't tell me what they are laughing about. None of them ask me round to their house after school like they used to. I feel lonely at school and at home.

Annabel didn't invite me out for her birthday. All my friends went to the cinema together and had a sleepover at Annabel's house without me. I cried all that evening. I felt really left out. I don't know what I've done wrong!

what can Olivia do?

Olivia hasn't done anything wrong. Her friends aren't behaving like good friends. She can:

★ talk about it with her teacher, her mum or dad or her big sister

★ think about how good friends behave:
   - good friends are kind to each other.
   - they share with each other.
   - they make each other feel happy.
   - they have fun together.

What Olivia did

I told my big sister Nina. She asked two girls in my class, Lee and Kerry, if I could play with them. They are really kind and good fun. I don't mind if my old friends leave me out now. I'm much happier with my new friends.

Nina's story

My little sister Olivia wasn't happy. She didn't want to go to school. I asked her what was wrong. She told me her friends weren't being kind to her. I said they weren't being good friends.

I asked her which children in her class were kind. She said Lee and Kerry were nice. So I helped her to make friends with Lee and Kerry. I'm glad she talked to me so I could help her. She doesn't mind going to school now.

WHAT IS BULLYING?

Bullying is when someone:

* makes you unhappy and thinks it's funny
* hurts you on purpose
* calls you names
* takes away your friends
* teases you and won't stop when you ask them to
* steals or spoils your things.

Bullying is always wrong. It's never your fault if you are bullied. If you are being bullied, don't keep it a secret. Tell someone who can help you do something to stop it happening.

I'M BULLIED ABOUT THE WAY I SPEAK

Jack has moved from one part of the country to another. The children at his new school laugh at the way he speaks. When this happens, he doesn't want to say anything.

Amir is Jack's classmate

Jack is the new boy in my class. Everyone laughs at his accent. They don't want to be his friend - just because he's different! I'd like to be his friend but I'm worried the other kids might start laughing at me too.

Amir

Jack's story

I had lots of friends at my old school. Then Dad got a new job and we moved a long way away.

The children at my new school tease me about my accent because it's different from theirs.

Every time I say something they imitate me and laugh! So now I don't say anything unless I really have to. I don't like being laughed at just because of the way I speak, but they won't stop it.

It's hard to make new friends if you can't say anything!

Jack

what can Jack do?

Remember, there's nothing wrong with him. He can:

★ tell his parents
★ tell his teacher
★ not be afraid to speak.

The children will get tired of imitating him every time he talks.

what Jack did

I told Mum and she talked to my teacher. He talked to the class about how boring it would be if everyone was exactly like them. He said I make the class much more interesting! We had a discussion about all the ways people can be different. Now no one imitates me and I talk all the time!

BIG GIRLS AT SCHOOL HURT ME!

Two older girls want to play with Emily every day. They treat her like a little doll. But they frighten Emily and sometimes they hurt her.

May is Emily's friend

Emily never wants to go out to play. She always wants to stay in and tidy the classroom.

When she does go out, she holds the hand of the grown-up on duty. I wish she'd play with me!

Emily

May

Emily's story

Every day at school, two big girls wait for me in the playground. They chase me and tickle me. They pick me up and swing me round. Sometimes they push and punch me.

They won't stop when I ask them to. They say it's only a game – but I don't like it. If I cry they call me a cry-baby!

If I say I'll tell my teacher, they call me a telltale!

They won't let me play with my own friends. I feel too frightened to go out to play.

What can Emily do?

Remember – it's not a game if you aren't having fun. She can:

* ★ tell her friend why she doesn't want to go out to play
* ★ tell her teacher
* ★ say she wants to play with her own friends and that she wants the big girls to leave her alone.

What Emily did

I told my friend May why I didn't want to go out to play. She said, "You're not a cry-baby or a telltale."

We told my teacher about the big girls and she talked to them. Now the grown-up on playground duty makes sure they leave me alone. I can play with my own friends again.

MY FRIENDS ARE BULLIES

Winnie's friends bully other children and make them unhappy. She knows it's wrong but doesn't try to stop them. Sometimes Winnie joins in. Lily is one of the children they bully.

Winnie

Lily

Lily's Story

I had nits and some girls in my class found out. They told everyone. They said, "Don't go near Lily, you'll get nits!"

Everyone kept out of my way. I felt really lonely and miserable.

15

Winnie's Story

Everyone wants to be in our gang at school because we're really cool! But sometimes my gang bullies other children. I don't like making anyone unhappy. Even though I know it's unkind I join in because, if I didn't, they might bully me! I want to stay part of the gang.

We bullied Lily for having nits. But we've all had nits before. It's not Lily's fault!

I know it's not cool to bully people. I want to stop bullying but I don't know how.

What can Winnie do?

She can:
* ★ tell her friends that she doesn't like bullying
* ★ make new friends if the children in the gang still want to be bullies
* ★ tell her teacher what is happening.

What Winnie did

I told the gang I wouldn't bully anyone again. They were cross but Amara agreed with me. Amara and I are best friends now. We aren't part of the gang and we've made new friends, like Lily. Together, we stand up for kids who are being bullied. We sometimes even play with the little kids. It isn't cool to bully.

Leo

Leo's story

My friends kept picking on a little kid in the playground. They said they were just teasing him. But when he got upset and cried, they didn't stop. At first I didn't do anything, but I felt bad. Even though I didn't join in, I felt as if I had been bullying him too.

In the end, I told my friends to leave the little kid alone. I took him to the teacher on duty. My friends stopped picking on him after that.

18

THEY MAKE FUN OF MY LUNCH!

Jade's story

My mum cooks everything for my lunch box. She won't give me food and drink in packets and cartons like everyone else has. Every day, some kids grab my lunch box. They open it and say, "What rubbish has Jade's mum made for her today?"

They drop my lunch on the floor. Sometimes they throw it away. I'm always hungry and I'm getting skinny!

I hate it when people are rude about my mum. I wish she would give me the same food as everyone else, but she says it's not good for me. I haven't told her what the kids do to my lunch!

What can Jade do?

She can:

* ★ be proud that her mum is a good cook and that she gives her healthy food
* ★ tell her mum she's being bullied about her lunch
* ★ tell her teacher what is happening.

What Jade did

I didn't tell my mum but I did tell my teacher. He talked to the class about healthy food. We did a class display of healthy foods. We even tried some and everyone liked something. They don't make rude comments about my food or throw it away any more.

I'M ALWAYS IN TROUBLE!

Freya did well at school. Now she keeps getting into trouble. She gets bad marks for her work. Her parents don't understand what has happened.

Aisha

Aisha is Freya's friend

My friend Freya writes brilliant stories and can do really hard sums in her head.

She used to come top in everything! But suddenly, she's doing really badly. For the first time ever, our teacher said she was disappointed with her work.

I don't know why she's changed.

Freya's Story

I like doing good work at school. I put my hand up first and get the answers right.

I get lots of smiley stickers and gold stars.

But then some kids in my class started calling me "Teacher's pet!" They hid my books. They threw my school bag in the bin. They said they'd beat me up if I told anyone. Now I don't work hard or put my hand up anymore.

They laugh at me when I get into trouble - which is all the time!

Freya

Giving in to the bullies isn't making Freya happy. She can:

★ remember, there's nothing wrong with working hard and doing well
★ tell her friend Aisha why she is getting bad marks
★ tell her parents and her teacher.

What Freya did

I told Mum and Dad about the bullies. They talked to my teacher. They all said I should be proud of doing well.

So I started working hard, but the bullies were worse than before!

So I told my teacher - again.

I don't know what she did, but the bullies suddenly stopped bullying me. I'm glad they didn't win.

$$84 + 43 = 127$$

$$233 - 62 = 171$$

$$27 = 0^2 + 1^2 + 1^2 + 5^2$$
$$= 0^2 + 3^2 + 3^2 + 3^2$$
$$= 1^2 + 1^2 + 3^2 + 4^2$$

$$12 \overline{)168} = 14$$

$$597 \times 7 = 4179$$

MY FRIEND BULLIES HIS BROTHER

My friend Marcus bullies his little brother Tommy. Marcus is really popular at school. Everyone wants to be his friend and he's my best friend. He's really nice to me - but he's nasty to Tommy. Sometimes he even hurts him and makes him cry.

He always does it when his mum and dad aren't there. He makes Tommy promise not to tell them. It's like he can be two different people - good friend Marcus and bully big brother Marcus.

I wish he'd be nice to Tommy.

What can Nat do?

He can:
* ★ tell Marcus he's being unkind to his brother
* ★ ask Marcus how he thinks Tommy feels
* ★ be nice to Tommy when he is at Marcus's house and stand up for him.

What Nat did

I told Marcus I thought he was being horrid to Tommy. I tried to make sure Marcus didn't bully Tommy when I was around. Marcus was cross with me. He said Tommy was really annoying and that it was all right for me, I didn't have to live with Tommy. But now he's started to be kinder so I'm really glad I said something.

Hey Marcus, you are being horrible to Tommy.

Marcus's story

I was the only child for a long time. Then Tommy arrived. Mum and Dad gave him all the love and attention. I wished Tommy had never been born and we could go back to the way we were before. I didn't realise I was bullying Tommy until Nat made me think. I don't like bullies!

Anyway, I suppose it's not Tommy's fault. Now I'm trying to be nicer to Tommy, he isn't quite so annoying!

26

HOW TO GET HELP IF YOU ARE BEING BULLIED

If you are being bullied, you can feel very lonely. If you talk to someone, they can help you. You could talk to your mum or dad or another grown-up in your family, your brother or sister or a friend.

Your school will have a policy on what to do about bullying, so you could talk to your teacher.

You may think that telling someone will only make things worse. If so, you can:

• ring Childline
• visit websites
(see page 31).
Remember, bullying is always wrong. You don't have to put up with it.

WE DEALT WITH RACISM

Jake used to bully Bertie, even though they were friends. Bertie was afraid of Jake.

Bertie: When I was new at school, Jake made friends with me. At first, I was really pleased to have a friend.

Jake: I didn't have any friends because I was a bully! Bertie didn't know that because he was new.

Bertie: At first, it was great. We did things together at school and went round to each other's houses to play.

Jake: I started to bully Bertie. I made him do everything I told him. I said I'd beat him up if he told on me or stopped being my friend.

Bertie: Jake frightened me and he wouldn't let me have any other friends. I wanted to stop being his friend but I didn't know how. In the end, I told my mum and dad.

Jake: Bertie's mum and dad came to talk to my mum and dad about me bullying Bertie. I was really angry. I thought - I'll get Bertie for this!

Bertie: I was glad I told Mum and Dad but I was afraid Jake would get me, just like he said he would if I told anyone.

Jake: To make things worse, my parents talked to my teacher! She told me that Bertie was only my friend because he was afraid of me. She made me say sorry to Bertie. She said if I "got" him, she'd know about it!

Bertie: After that I just wanted to keep out of Jake's way. But Jake really changed and he tried to be nice to me.

Jake: I didn't want to bully kids into being my friends any more. I wanted to have real friends who actually liked me. So I had to get nicer!

Bertie: It took a bit of time, but Jake and me are friends again. We've both got other friends too. The best thing is, Jake isn't a bully any more and I'm not being bullied.

GLOSSARY

Bullying
Bullying is when someone hurts you or makes you unhappy and afraid on purpose.

Gang
A gang is a group of friends who go round together and play together.

Giving in
You give in to someone when they make you do something you don't want to do.

Lonely
You can feel lonely when you don't have many friends and spend a lot of time on your own.

Policy
A policy is a set of ideas and rules. A school bullying policy sets out what should be done if anyone is being bullied at school.

Popular
Someone is popular when people like them and they have a lot of friends.

Proud
You feel proud when you are pleased with something you have done and are happy for other people to know about it.

Secret
When you have a secret, you keep something to yourself and don't tell anyone about it.

Share
You share when you tell or give things to other people and you don't keep things to yourself.

Unkind
You are unkind when you do or say something that makes someone else unhappy.

FURTHER INFORMATION

For children

www.childline.org.uk
Helpline: 0800 1111
Childline is a free helpline for children in the UK. You can talk to someone about any problem and they will help you to sort it out.

www.kidshealth.org/kid/feeling/emotion/bullies.html
Learn about bullies and how to deal with them.

www.kidscape.org.uk
A website helping to prevent bullying.

For parents

www.familylives.org.uk
Helpline for parents:
0808 800 2222
Family Lives offers advice, guidance and support for parents who are concerned about their children. The 'Bullying UK' section offers advice for parents whose children are being bullied at school.

For readers in Australia and New Zealand

https://kidshelpline.com.au
Online and phone help for a wide range of issues.

www.cyh.com
Loads of online information about all sorts of issues, including bullying.

www.kidsline.org.nz
A helpline run by specially trained young volunteers to help kids and teens deal with troubling issues and problems.

INDEX

Notes for parents, carers and teachers

When children are bullied, they need the support of adults to help them deal with it. But they are often reluctant to talk about it. Depression, low self-esteem and poor results at school can be signs that they are being bullied.

- Adults can look out for signs that a child is being bullied.
- Children need to know that being bullied is not their fault.
- Bullying should always be taken seriously.
- Fear of making things worse can stop children telling anyone.

They need to know that it's best to tell an adult, who will take effective action where necessary.

Page 4 Olivia's story

Olivia is feeling lonely and left out of her group of friends at school.

- Knowing what makes a friend a good friend can help children to choose their friends well and to be a good friend to other children.

Page 10 Jack's story

Jack is unhappy because the children at his new school laugh at him for being different.

- Understanding that being different is not wrong can help children to appreciate other people and to build their own self-confidence.

Page 13 Emily's story

Emily is frightened to go out to play at school because bigger children are bullying her.

- Children need effective intervention from an adult if they are being bullied by bigger children.

Page 16 Winnie's story

Winnie's friends are bullies. She knows it's wrong to join in but doesn't know how to stop.

- Adults can make it clear that bullying is unacceptable and never cool, and support a child who wants to stop bullying.

Page 19 Jade's story

Jade is being bullied because she brings healthy food to school for lunch.

- Being different, for example by eating healthy food, is not wrong. An adult can help tackle the bullies and protect the child who is different.

Page 22 Freya's story

Freya is deliberately doing badly at school so that other children don't call her 'teacher's pet'.

- It's hard for children to stand up to bullies on their own. An adult can support children and help them not to give in to bullies.

Page 24 Nat's story

Marcus doesn't realise he is bullying his little brother.

- Children can be bullies without meaning to be. An adult can point out what they are doing and help them to change their behaviour.

Page 28 Playscript, Jake and Bertie's story

Children could perform the parts in this simple playscript and then discuss what happened to each character, including possible reasons why Jake was a bully and what it did to his friendships.

These are the list of contents for the
titles in the Dealing With series.

Dealing With Bullying

I feel left out * What is bullying?
* I'm bullied about the way I
speak * Big girls at school hurt
me! * My friends are bullies *
They make fun of my lunch! * I'm
always in trouble! * My friend
bullies his brother * How to get
help if you are being bullied * We
beat bullying: playscript.

Dealing With Our New Baby

I don't want a new baby! * Expecting
a baby * I'm worried that Mum and
the baby won't be all right * Getting
ready for the baby * The new baby's
boring! * I'm jealous of the new baby
* My baby brother's a nuisance! * I
want to help! * Watching a baby grow
* My little sister always gets her own
way! * Will my stepdad still love me?
* Our new baby: playscript

Dealing With My Parents' Divorce

My home isn't a happy place to be any
more * What is divorce? * My parents
are getting a divorce * I feel angry
with my mum and dad * Is my parents'
divorce my fault? * What's going to
happen to me? * I'm ashamed about my
parents' divorce * How can I love both
my mum and dad? * Will we be happy
again? * It happened to us: playscript.

Dealing With My Stepfamily

What is a stepfamily? *
Everything's changing! * My
stepdad's not my real dad * Will
my stepmum stay with us? * I
feel left out * Why do I have
to share? * My stepmum's rules
aren't fair! * I like my stepdad
better than my real dad * We're
good friends now: playscript

Dealing With When People Die

I don't know what is happening! *
What is death? * I don't want to
say goodbye! * What happens at a
funeral? * I'm angry with my brother
for leaving me * Will I ever stop
feeling sad? * I'm afraid I will die
too * My parents don't love me now
* I miss granddad too * How can I
remember someone special? * When
our friend died: playscript

Dealing With Racism

I'm new in this country and at
school * We are different and
the same * I'm left out *
What is racism? * It's my name
too! * Celebrations * Racism is
making my friend unhappy * I'm
in a gang * I'm scared * Racism
in schools * We dealt with
racism: playscript